God knows what's best for me

by Denise Vezey
Illustrated by Victoria Ponikvar Frazier

Equipping Kids for Life

A Faith Parenting Guide can be found on page 31.

Dedication:
To my Father, David Naumann—
"Father Knows Best!"

Faith Kids® is an imprint of
Cook Communications Ministries, Colorado Springs, CO 80918
Cook Communications, Paris, Ontario
Kingsway Communications, Eastbourne, England

GOD KNOWS WHAT'S BEST FOR ME
© 2001 by Denise Vezey for text and Victoria Ponikvar-Frazier for illustrations

Edited by Jeannie Harmon
Designed by Sonya Design and Illustration

First printing, 2001
Printed in Canada
05 04 30 02 01   5 4 3 2 1

ISBN 0-7814-3503-X

99-17033
CIP

Table öf Cöntents

My new placë to live

I am very sad today.

Our family is moving!

I'll miss my school and friends.

Mommy says, "God knows best."

But I don't think He does.

I sort, I pick, I pack.
I throw things in a sack.

God in His wisdom
knows what to give.
But, I don't want to find
a new place to live.

"Goodbye, little snow blue birds.
Goodbye, dear tree.
I'll miss playing hide and seek
and swinging from your branches."

"It's time to go," Mommy calls.
We get in our car and drive far, far away.

At last we arrive.
It is dark and cold.
"Don't worry," Mommy says cheerfully.
"We'll be warm and cozy in no time."

The next day, I hear a knock at our door.
A girl just my age asks,
"Do you want to play?"
"Mommy, may I?"
"That would be fine." Mommy smiles.

First we pretend to swim
in the tall grass behind our house.
Next, we play piggly-wiggly with our toes
and find pictures in the clouds.
I never had so much fun!

That night in bed,
I can leave the light on
and read before I fall asleep.
I could *never* do that before.
My little sister always slept with me.
I'm so happy we moved.

I look, I pick, I stack.
I pull things out of my sack.

God in His wisdom
knew what to give.
I'm thankful He found us
a new place to live.

My ride on the slide

Don't you just love going down a slide?

It is slippery and fast.

You race around the curves

and the world flies by. *Whee-ee-ee!*

I could do this forever.

climb up to the sky.
slip, I float, I fly.

Up in the air
I sail and I glide.
I like to be first
when I ride on a slide.

Today Daddy is putting up my slide.
My new friends and I
can't wait to go down it.
When it's ready, I'm going first!

"It's *my* house and *my* slide," I say.

"I'm first!"

My new friends look at me funny.

They say, "Okay. Have it your way."

I run up the slide and go down.
Then I push my way to the front again.

Pretty soon, no one's left but me!
"Dad-dy," I cry. "Where did everybody go?"

"I think they went to Tammy's house, dear."

"But, why?" I ask.

"Well," Daddy says, "maybe Tammy
knows how to take turns and share.
It isn't much fun to be with a me-first girl."

"Honey, God tells us in the Bible
to put others first.
We always feel better
when we do what God tells us to do.
He knows the best way for us to live."

"Oh, Daddy, do you think
they will give me another chance?"
"Give it a try," he smiles.
"Girlfriends. . . . Oh, girlfriends," I call.
"Please come back.
I'm sorry I wasn't very nice."

We climb up to the sky.
We slip, we float, we fly.

Up in the air
I sail and I glide.
I don't have to be first
when I ride on my slide.

My visit to the nurse

Today I have to visit the nurse.
I need some shots for school.
I hate shots.
If I didn't go to school,
I could skip my shots!

I whine, I moan, I sigh.
I look Mom in the eye.

"If you really love me,
you won't make me cry.
You'll tell that old nurse
we're leaving, good-bye!"

"Come on, Sweet Pea," Mommy says.

"It won't be so bad."

"I don't want to get a shot," I cry back.

"I'm sure you don't," Mom replies.

"No one does."

"If you're brave, I'll get you an ice cream cone when you're done."

It's hard to get a shot when I don't feel sick.
Get me out of here!

Mommy gives me a hug.
"Sometimes we have to do
things that don't feel good
because they are good for us.
God is wise. He knows what is best for us."

"If you get a shot now,
it may hurt a little,
but it will keep you from getting sick,
and that would hurt a lot."

The nurse calls our name.

Uh-oh. It's my turn to get a shot!

I ask the nurse, "Will it hurt?"
"Maybe a little bit," she says.

"I have pretty stickers for all
of the big girls who get a shot today.
Now, try to be brave.
This will be over as quick as a wink."

I hold my breath, I pray.
I squeeze Mom's hand, I say,

"Since God really loves me
Sometimes I may cry.
But I can trust Him,
For He is so wise."

Dear God, it makes me happy to know that I can trust You in every way, because You are so wise. Amen.

"And we know that in all things God works for the good of those who love him."
Romans 8:28 (NIV)

Faith Parenting Guide

God Knows What's Best for Me

Age: 4-7

Life issue: To learn that God knows best will take care of even unhappy situations.

Spiritual Building Block: Trust

Learning Styles
Help your children learn about wisdom in the following ways:

Sight: Look back at the illustrations with your children and discuss how God turned unhappy situations into blessings.

Sound: Discuss with your children how we can't know all of God's love without facing tough situations. For example, in the little girl's tough situation with having to move she found out just how much God cares about her and loves her. Tell your children some of the accounts in the Bible that show God's wisdom and sovereignty; such as Abraham and Sarah, David and Goliath, and Daniel in the lion's den.

Touch: The Bible is filled with verses that tell us about God's wisdom. Look up and memorize verses such as Ephesians 4:32, Philippians 2:14a, or Mark 12:31. Talk about their meaning with your children and suggest ways to demonstrate the wisdom found in these verses.